THE IRISH AND GO DIARY 2008

COMPILED BY

GLENDA DEVLIN

FOR TOMMY - MY INSPIRATION

You were my strength, when I was weak
You were my voice when I couldn't speak
You were my eyes when I couldn't see
You saw the best there was in me
Because you loved me

First Published in 2003 by Glenda Devlin
Revised Editions: 2004; 2005; 2006;2007;2008

ISBN 0-9554223-0-2
978-0-9554223-0-0

Design and Origination: Glenda Devlin
Cover Design: Brendan and Adrian Sands

Printed in the Republic of Ireland by
Colour Books, Dublin

Published by:
CHICCO
8 Burma Road, Strandhill,
Co. Sligo, Ireland

www.getupandgodiary.com

info@chiccoonline.com

Forgive the past – Let it go
Live the present – The power of Now
Create the future – Thoughts become things

An Irish Blessing

May your neighbours respect you,
Troubles neglect you,
The angels protect you,
And Heaven accept you.

YOUR DIARY CONTAINS
130 PAGES OF INSPIRATION!

ENJOY EVERY PAGE!

This Diary Belongs to: _____

Address: _____

_____

Telephone: _____

E-mail: _____

THIS DIARY CONTAINS

Messages to those who mean a lot to you.
Wisdom to those who have touched your
  life when you needed it.
Humour for those who make you
  smile when you are down.
Optimism for those who have made
  you see the brighter side.
Love and caring for those you want to
  tell how you appreciate their friendship.
Inspiration when you need it.

Photographer: Merwelien van der Merwe

2008

Forgive the past – Let it go
Live the present – The power of Now
Create the future – Thoughts become things

January

M	T	W	T	F	S	S
	1	2	3	4	5	6
7	8	9	10	11	12	13
14	15	16	17	18	19	20
21	22	23	24	25	26	27
28	29	30	31			

February

M	T	W	T	F	S	S
				1	2	3
4	5	6	7	8	9	10
11	12	13	14	15	16	17
18	19	20	21	22	23	24
25	26	27	28	29		

March

M	T	W	T	F	S	S
					1	2
3	4	5	6	7	8	9
10	11	12	13	14	15	16
17	18	19	20	21	22	23
24	25	26	27	28	29	30
31						

April

M	T	W	T	F	S	S
1	2	3	4	5	6	
7	8	9	10	11	12	13
14	15	16	17	18	19	20
21	22	23	24	25	26	27
28	29	30				

May

M	T	W	T	F	S	S
			1	2	3	4
5	6	7	8	9	10	11
12	13	14	15	16	17	18
19	20	21	22	23	24	25
26	27	28	29	30	31	

June

M	T	W	T	F	S	S
						1
2	3	4	5	6	7	8
9	10	11	12	13	14	15
16	17	18	19	20	21	22
23	24	25	26	27	28	29
30						

July

M	T	W	T	F	S	S
1	2	3	4	5	6	
7	8	9	10	11	12	13
14	15	16	17	18	19	20
21	22	23	24	25	26	27
28	29	30	31			

August

M	T	W	T	F	S	S
				1	2	3
4	5	6	7	8	9	10
11	12	13	14	15	16	17
18	19	20	21	22	23	24
25	26	27	28	29	30	31

September

M	T	W	T	F	S	S
1	2	3	4	5	6	7
8	9	10	11	12	13	14
15	16	17	18	19	20	21
22	23	24	25	26	27	28
29	30					

October

M	T	W	T	F	S	S
	1	2	3	4	5	
6	7	8	9	10	11	12
13	14	15	16	17	18	19
20	21	22	23	24	25	26
27	28	29	30	31		

November

M	T	W	T	F	S	S
					1	2
3	4	5	6	7	8	9
10	11	12	13	14	15	16
17	18	19	20	21	22	23
24	25	26	27	28	29	30

December

M	T	W	T	F	S	S
1	2	3	4	5	6	7
8	9	10	11	12	13	14
15	16	17	18	19	20	21
22	23	24	25	26	27	28
29	30	31				

BANK AND PUBLIC HOLIDAYS

REPUBLIC OF IRELAND

New Years Day, 1 January; St Patrick's Day, 17 March;
Good Friday, 21 March; Easter Monday, 24 March; May Holiday,
5 May; June Holiday, 2 June; August Holiday, 4 August;
Halloween, 27 October; Christmas Day, 25 December;
St Stephen's Day, 26 December.

ENGLAND, SCOTLAND AND WALES

New Years Day, 1 January; Good Friday, 21 March; Easter Monday,
24 March; May Holiday, 5 May; Spring Bank Holiday, 26 May;
Summer Bank Holiday, 25 August; Christmas Day, 25 December;
Boxing Day, 26 December.

NORTHERN IRELAND

New Years Day, 1 January; St Patrick's Day, 17 March; Good Friday,
21 March; Easter Monday 24 March; May Holiday, 5 May;
Spring Bank Holiday, 26 May; Orangeman's Holiday, 14 July;
Summer Bank Holiday, 25 August; Christmas Day, 25 December;
Boxing Day, 26 December.

Emergency Telephone Numbers

January

Every day is a gift from God, that is why it is called 'The Present'

Let me give thanks for a New Year. For happy memories, for things, people and places I never want to forget. May this new year be a good year. Bless those who will share the comings and goings of my life, and those with whom I live, work and play. Set laughter on my lips and a twinkle in my eye.

TUESDAY 1
Ponder over some goals

WEDNESDAY 2
Learn from your mistakes

THURSDAY 3
Know when to let go

We cannot discover new oceans until we have the courage to lose sight of the shore

Desiderata

Go Placidly amid the noise and haste, and
remember what peace there may be in silence.
As far as possible without surrender be on good terms with all
persons. Speak your truth quietly and clearly, & listen to
others, even the dull and ignorant; they too have their story.
Avoid loud and aggressive persons, they are vexations to the
spirit. If you compare yourself with others, you may become
vain and bitter; for always there will be greater and lesser
persons than yourself. Enjoy your achievements as well as your
plans. Keep interested in your own career, however humble; it
is a real possession in the changing fortunes of time. Exercise
caution in your business affairs; for the world is full of trickery.
But let this not blind you to what virtue there is; many persons
strive for high ideals; and everywhere life is full of heroism. Be
yourself. Especially, do not feign affection. Neither be cynical
about love; for in the face of all aridity and disenchantment it is
perennial as the grass. Take kindly the counsel of the years,
gracefully surrendering the things of youth. Nurture strength of
spirit to shield you in sudden misfortune. But do not distress
yourself with imaginings. Many fears are born of fatigue and
loneliness. Beyond a wholesome discipline, be gentle with
yourself. You are a child of the universe, no less than the trees
and the stars; you have a right to be here. And whether or not
it is clear to you, no doubt the universe is unfolding as it should.
Therefore be at peace with God, whatever you conceive Him
to be, and whatever your labours and aspirations, in the noisy
confusion of life keep peace with your soul. With all its sham,
drudgery and broken dreams, it is still a beautiful world.
Be careful. Strive to be happy.

Nobody can
Make you feel
Inferior without
Your consent
ELEANOR ROOSEVELT

January

The smallest actual good is better than the most magnificent promises of possibilities.

Thomas Macaulay

FRIDAY 4
Make a list of all your blessings

SATURDAY 5
Someone that you don't even know exists, loves you

SUNDAY 6
Take one day at a time

It's not the score
That makes us great,
Nor is it the wealth
We strive to create.
But that we live our lives
In pursuit of the truth,
And honour our dreams
We dreamt in our youth.
Mike Dooley

January

Laughter helps to heal tears

Good ideas will not work unless you do

Rules for a Happy Home
When

you Get it out – use it
you Sleep on in – make it up
you Wear it – hang it up
you Drop it – pick it up
you Dirty it – wash it
you Open it – close it
you Turn it on – turn it off
it Rings – answer it
it's Empty – fill it
it Howls – feed it
it Needs love –

hug and kiss it

BE LESS CURIOUS ABOUT PEOPLE AND MORE
CURIOUS ABOUT IDEAS – *Marie Curry*

WHAT SPIDER SOLITAIRE
TAUGHT ME ABOUT LIFE!

1. It's a good feeling when a plan comes together.
2. If you create an empty space you can work wonders.
3. If you lose a game it doesn't mean you're no good.
4. When you win you want to try again.
5. There is a sequence to things.
6. Take a break and you'll find new opportunities.
7. Have a plan before you make a move.
8. You cannot win unless you get rid of the baggage.
9. Concentrate on what you're doing.
10. Don't use all the given advice it causes bad moves.
11. When you don't know what to do next seek advice.
12. You have to make the most of the cards you're dealt.
13. Winning comes easy when you're not tired.
14. Winning isn't everything, enjoy the getting there.
15. Don't waste time playing games when you should
    BE DOING MORE IMPORTANT THINGS!!

January

A friend is someone who knows the song in your heart, and can sing it back to you when you have forgotten the words.

TUESDAY 8	
	Judge less
WEDNESDAY 9	
	A tidy house is a tidy mind
THURSDAY 10	
	Every effect has a cause
FRIDAY 11	
	Phone a friend and tell them how much they mean to you
SATURDAY 12	
	Remember, you mean the world to someone

WHATEVER HAPPENS TO YOU IN LIFE DOESN'T MATTER
IT IS YOUR ATTITUDE TOWARDS IT THAT MAKES THE DIFFERENCE.

January

Sometimes our light goes out but it is blown into flame again by another human being. Each of us owes deepest thanks to those who have rekindled this light.

Albert Schweitzer

SUNDAY 13
Dream of new ideals
MONDAY 14
Join an evening class for a few weeks
TUESDAY 15
Explore new possibilities

Life is a challenge, meet it.
Life is a gift, accept it.
Life is an adventure, dare it.
Life is a sorrow, overcome it.
Life is a tragedy, face it.

Life is a game, play it.
Life is a mystery, unfold it.
Life is an opportunity, take it.
Life is a journey, complete it.
Life is a song, sing it.

January

COURAGE doesn't always roar, sometimes courage is the little voice at the end of the day that says: "I'll try again tomorrow"

WEDNESDAY 16
When life hands you lemons, ask for Tequila
THURSDAY 17
Opportunity can knock very softy
FRIDAY 18
What ever you do, do it well
SATURDAY 19
Self expression is essential to life
SUNDAY 20
Remember smooth seas never make skilful sailors

The happiest people do not have the best of everything, they just make the most of everything that comes their way.

Goals are not only absolutely necessary to motivate us. They are essential to really keep us alive.

Robert Schuller

ABOUT CHILDREN

Your children are not your children.
They are the sons and daughters of Life's longing for itself.
They came through you but not from you
And though they are with you yet they belong not to you.
You may give them your love but not your thoughts,
For they have their own thoughts.
You may house their bodies but not their souls,
For their souls dwell in the house of tomorrow,
which you cannot visit, not even in your dreams.
You may strive to be like them,
but seek not to make them like you,
For life goes not backward nor tarries with yesterday.
You are the bows from which your children as living
arrows are sent forth.
The Prophet (1923) – KAHLIL GIBRAN

January

DO ALL THE GOOD YOU CAN
BY ALL THE MEANS YOU CAN
IN ALL THE WAYS YOU CAN
IN ALL THE PLACES YOU CAN
TO ALL THE PEOPLE YOU CAN
AS LONG AS EVER YOU CAN

MONDAY 21

Enthusiasm for life reflects positively on your health

TUESDAY 22

Leave a house key with a neighbour

WEDNESDAY 23

Love is giving without expecting a return

THURSDAY 24

Never leave until tomorrow what you can do today

FRIDAY 25

You are special and unique

SATURDAY 26

Fill a clothes bag for charity

ALL THAT YOU GIVE IS GIVEN TO YOURSELF

January

You don't stop laughing because you grow old. You grow old because you stop laughing.

SUNDAY 27

Don't indulge in junk culture

MONDAY 28

Bad money habits are serious

TUESDAY 29

Start a savings plan

WEDNESDAY 30

One who looks for a friend without failures will find none

COMMITMENT is what transforms a promise into reality
COMMITMENT is making the time when there is none.
COMMITMENT is the stuff that character is made of.

January

Those who thrive on hatred destroy their own capacity to make a positive contribution.

Nelson Mandela

THURSDAY 31

Do not let regrets take the place of dreams

GOALS FOR FEBRUARY

TO HAVE COURAGE FOR WHATEVER COMES IN LIFE – EVERYTHING LIES IN THAT.

SAINT THERESA OF AVILA

WHAT WE SEE IS WHAT WE GET!

Age 3: She looks at herself and sees a Queen.

Age 8: She looks at herself and sees Cinderella.

Age 15: She looks at herself and sees an Ugly Sister (Mum I can't go to school looking like this!)

Age 20: She looks at herself and sees "too fat/too thin, too short/too tall, too straight/too curly" – but decides she's going out anyway.

Age 30: She looks at herself and sees "too fat/too thin, too short/too tall, too straight/too curly" – but decides she doesn't have time to fix it, so she goes out anyway.

Age 40: She looks at herself and sees "clean" and goes out anyway.

Age 50: She looks at herself and sees "I am" and goes wherever she wants to go.

Age 60: She looks at herself and reminds herself of all the people who can't even see themselves in the mirror anymore, goes out and conquers the world.

Age 70: She looks at herself and sees wisdom, laughter and ability, goes out and enjoys life.

Age 80: Doesn't bother to look. Just puts on a purple hat and goes out to have fun with the world.

FEBRUARY

Develop confidence in yourself and act as if you have it until you do.

Barbara Krouse

FRIDAY 1

Make a few honest mistakes and learn

SATURDAY 2

We become what we think about

To GoD.CoM

Dear Lord,
There's one important thing that I wish that you could do.
Please don't mind my asking . . . bless my computer too!
Now I know it is unusual to bless a motherboard
But listen just a second while I explain I to you Lord . . .

You see that little metal box holds more than odds and ends
Inside those small compartments rest so many of my friends.
I know so much about them by the kindness that they give
And this little scrap of metal takes me to where they live.

Amen

FEBRUARY

Now is the time to let go of the worn-out, the painful and the sad, and to cross the threshold into a new era of promise.

SUNDAY 3	
	Keep your mind active
MONDAY 4	
	Forgive and forget
TUESDAY 5	
	Put flowers in your bedroom
WEDNESDAY 6	
	Be positive and encouraging to your family

THERE ARE PEOPLE WHO HAVE MONEY AND THERE ARE PEOPLE WHO ARE RICH.   *Coco Chanel*

FEBRUARY

We are not governed by politicians but by ideas.

THURSDAY 7

Good taste is never out of fashion

FRIDAY 8

There is no such thing as a "little" thing

SATURDAY 9

Even the strongest child needs loving support

SUNDAY 10

Keep work at work

A GOOD BARGAIN

I bargained with life for a penny,

And life would pay no more,

However I begged at evening

When I counted my scanty store.

For life is a just employer,

He gives what you ask,

But once you have set the wages,

Why, you must bear the task.

I worked for a menial's hire,

Only to learn, dismayed,

That any wage I asked of life

Life would have paid.

Jessie B. Rittenhouse

These are a few of my favourite things!

Maalox and nose drops and needles for knitting,
Walkers and handrails and new dental fittings,
Bundles of magazines tied up with string,
These are a few of my favourite things.

Cadillacs, cataracts, hearing aids and glasses,
Polident, Fixodent and false teeth in glasses,
Pacemakers, golf carts and porches with swings,
These are a few of my favourite things.

When the pipes leak,
When the bones creak,
When the knees go bad,
I simply remember my favourite things,
And then I don't feel so bad

Hot tea and crumpets and corn pads for bunions,
No spicy hot food or food cooked with onions,
Bathrobes and heat pads and hot meals they bring,
These are a few of my favourite things.

Back pains, confused brains and no fear of sinning,
Thin bones and fractures and hair that is thinning,
We don't mention our short shrunken frames,
When we remember our favourite things.

When the joints ache,
When the hips break,
When the eyes grow dim,
Then I remember the great life I've had,
And then I don't feel so bad!

FEBRUARY

The best vitamin for making friends is B1.

MONDAY 11

Start a Birthday Book

TUESDAY 12

Quiet reflection may be of great help today

WEDNESDAY 13

All things start with a thought

THURSDAY 14

Good enough never is

FRIDAY 15

Plan a holiday

SATURDAY 16

Learn to make your own greeting cards

To keep your mind clean and healthy, change
it every once in a while.

FEBRUARY

An optimist sees an opportunity in every calamity; a pessimist sees a calamity in every opportunity.

SUNDAY 17
Take time off from structured activities
MONDAY 18
Drink more water
TUESDAY 19
Take care of your body

MAKING LIFE WORTHWHILE

It is not what the world
gives me
In honour, praise or gold
It is what I give the world,
So others do unfold.

If by my work through life, I can
Another soul unfold,
Then I have done what cannot be
Made good by praise or gold.

One tiny thought or a tiny word
May give a great thought birth,
And if that thought was caused by
me, **I've lived a life of worth.**

Richard F. Wolfe

FEBRUARY

Where there is peace and meditation, there is neither anxiety nor doubt.
Saint Francis of Assisi (1181–1226)

WEDNESDAY 20
A smile can be priceless

THURSDAY 21
Make a dental appointment

FRIDAY 22
Begin with the end in mind

I WANT TO LIVE ONLY FOR ECSTACY. SMALL DOSES, MODERATE LOVES, ALL HALF SHADES LEAVE ME COLD. I LIKE EXTRAVAGANCE, LETTERS WHICH GIVE THE POSTMAN A STIFF BACK TO CARRY, BOOKS WHICH OVERFLOW FROM THEIR COVERS, SEXUALITY WHICH BURSTS THE THERMOMETERS. *ANAÏS NON*

 The person who pulls the oars has no time to rock the boat.

 The gifts we have can also be a gift to others.

The only way to stop the war is to stop hating the enemy.

Pema Chödrön

 Learn something from the way other people do things.

Think big thoughts but enjoy small pleasures.

If I Could Raise
My Children Over Again

If I had my children to raise all over again …
I'd build self-esteem first, and the house later.
I'd finger paint more, and point my finger less.
I'd do less correcting, and more connecting.
I'd take my eyes off my watch,
and watch with my eyes.
I would care to know less, and know to care more.
I'd take more hikes and fly more kites.
I'd stop playing serious, and seriously play.
I would run through more fields
and gaze at more stars.
I'd do more hugging, and less tugging.
I'd see the oak tree in the acorn more often.
I would be firm less often, and affirm much more.
I'd model less about the "Love Of Power,"
And more about the "Power Of LOVE."
~ Dianne Loomans ~

 **FEBRUARY**

If you want
to be loved -
Be loveable

SATURDAY 23	
	Allow some fresh air into your house
SUNDAY 24	
	Happy times are best when shared
MONDAY 25	
	Only you can make the difference
TUESDAY 26	
	When in doubt take courage
WEDNESDAY 27	
	Make new friends but cherish the old ones

Life is one big canvas,
throw all the paint you can on it.
Danny Kaye

FEBRUARY

People will forget what you said, people will forget what you did, but people will never forget how you made them feel.

THURSDAY 28

Life always gives you a second chance

FRIDAY 29

Isn't this the day she can ask him to marry her?

MEN ARE LIKE BUSSES!

Men are like busses
You wait for about a year
As soon as one approaches your stop
Two or three others appear.

You look at them flashing their indicators,
Offering you a ride.
You're trying to read the destinations,
You haven't much time to decide.

If you make a mistake, there is no turning back.
Jump off, and you'll stand there and gaze
While the cars and the taxis and the lorries go by
And the minutes, the hours, the days.

Wendy Cope

You are guided
by your mind

FAIRIES CAN FLY
BECAUSE THEY
TAKE THEMSELVES
SO LIGHTLY

<u>GOALS FOR THIS MONTH</u>

To make an omelette you
have to break eggs!

The more passions and desires one has,
the more ways one has of being happy.

*Charlotte-Catherine 17th-Century
Princess of Monaco*

 **MARCH**

People, for the sake of earning a living forget to live. *Margaret Fuller*

 Don't walk in front of me, I may not follow.
Don't walk behind me, I may not lead.
Just walk beside me and be my friend.

SATURDAY 1   Begin where you are now
SUNDAY 2   Never confuse problems with inconvenience
MONDAY 3   You have a right to say no
TUESDAY 4   Self expression is essential to life

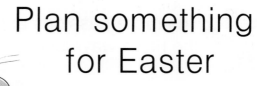

Plan something for Easter

DEDICATE TIME TO:

1. **WORK**
   - It's the price of success

2. **THINK**
   - It's the fountain of power

3. **ENJOY**
   - It's the secret of youth

4. **READ**
   - It's the basis of knowledge

5. **WORSHIP**
   - It's the path to salvation

6. **HAVE FRIENDS**
   - It's the path to happiness

7. **LOVE AND BE LOVED**
   - It's the source of joy and satisfaction

8. **DREAM**
   - It raises your soul to the stars

9. **LAUGH**
   - It mitigates the stress in your life

10. **PLAN**
    - It's the secret to find time for the previous 9 things.

IF A DOG COULD TEACH US

we would learn such things as:

- When loved ones come home, always run and greet them.
- Take naps and stretch before rising.
- Run, romp and play daily
- Avoid biting when a growl will do.
- Delight in the simple joy of a long walk.
- Be loyal.
- Never pretend to be something you're not.
- If what you want lies buried, dig until you find it.
- Fresh air and wind in your hair is ecstasy.
- When someone is having a bad day, be silent, sit close to them, and nuzzle them gently.

MARCH

Many people would rather die than think, and usually they do!

WEDNESDAY 5	
	Sometimes there is no race to be won
THURSDAY 6	
	Always be on time
FRIDAY 7	
	Keep a promise to yourself
SATURDAY 8	
	Thoughts are seeds and seeds are deeds
SUNDAY 9	
	The oak tree is in the acorn
MONDAY 10	
	Make a will

Moving on is far more productive than hanging on.

MARCH

> The best thing about the future is that it comes only one day at a time.
> *Abraham Lincoln*

TUESDAY 11

Go for a long walk and enjoy the scenery

A STORY ABOUT ANGER

There was a little boy with a bad temper. His father gave him a bag of nails and told him that, every time he lost his temper, to hammer a nail into the back fence.
The first day the boy had driven 37 nails into the fence. Then it gradually dwindled down. He discovered it was easier to hold his temper than to drive those nails into the fence. Finally the day came that when the boy didn't lose his temper at all. He told his father about it and the father suggested that the boy now pull out one nail for each day that he was able to hold his temper.
The days passed and the young boy was finally able to tell his father that all the nails were gone. The father took his son by the hand and led him to the fence.
He said, "You have done well my son, but look at all the holes in the fence. The fence will never be the same again. When you say things in anger, they leave a scar, just like this one."
You can put a knife in a man and draw it out. It won't matter how many times you say you're sorry, the wound will always be there.
A verbal wound is as bad as a physical one."

 **MARCH**

It is from your peace
of mind that a peaceful
world arises.

A Course In Miracles

WEDNESDAY 12

Do something really different

THURSDAY 13

Isolation leads to self confrontation –
it is important to spend time alone

FRIDAY 14

Practise to be patient

SATURDAY 15

Seek to understand more

SUNDAY 16

Ninety percent of what you worry about never happens

 May the saddest day of your
future be no worse than the
happiest day of your past.

 **MARCH**

**A man never discloses his own character
so clearly as when he describes another's.**
Jean Paul Richter

MONDAY 17

IT'S PADDY'S DAY!!

Phone a relative you seldom speak to

TUESDAY 18

The more mistakes you make the more you learn

WEDNESDAY 19

Pass a compliment – it's uplifting

THURSDAY 20

Plant something

"Would you tell me please which way I
ought to walk from here?"
"That depends a good deal on where you
want to get to" said the Cat
"I don't much care where" said Alice
"Then it does not matter which way
you walk" said the Cat.   *Alice in Wonderland*

DO GOOD ANYWAY!

People are often unreasonable, illogical, and self-centred
- Forgive them anyway.

If you are kind, people may accuse you of selfish, ulterior
motives - Be kind anyway.

If you are successful, you will win some false friends and some
true enemies - Succeed anyway.

If you are honest and frank, people may cheat you
- Be honest and frank anyway.

What you spend years building, someone could destroy
overnight - Build anyway.

If you find serenity and happiness, they may be jealous
- Be happy anyway.

The good you do today, people will often forget tomorrow
- Do good anyway.

Give the world the best you have, it
may never be enough
- Give the world the best you have anyway.

You see, in the final analysis it is between
you and God.
It was never between you and them anyway.

MARCH

Kindness in words,
creates confidence.
Kindness in thinking,
creates profoundness.
Kindness in giving,
creates love.

FRIDAY 21

Adversity introduces us to ourselves

SATURDAY 22

Have dinner by candle light

SUNDAY 23

Bake something

MONDAY 24

Neither a borrower nor a lender be

TUESDAY 25

Wash your car

You are the creator of your own reality. You attract the events of your life through the beliefs you accept as truth. Choose your beliefs consciously, carefully, and joyously!

MARCH

I like not only to be loved, but to be told that I am loved; The realm of silence is large enough beyond the grave.

GEORGE ELLIOT

WEDNESDAY 26

Still to do comes from doing

THURSDAY 27

A family is a strong support network

FRIDAY 28

There is more pleasure in giving than there is in receiving

SATURDAY 29

Get enough sleep

SUNDAY 30

You need a lot of patience to build a relationship

Holding a grudge is tiring
Rise above it

MARCH

Work on yourself
When we habitually set aside time to be quiet and simply listen, a new awareness develops.

Promises may get friends,
'tis performance that keeps them"
Benjamin Franklin

MONDAY 31

Try a Yoga class

GOOD MOTTO TO LIVE BY:

Life should not be a journey to the grave with the intention of arriving safely in an attractive and well preserved body, but rather to skid in sideways,

Champagne in one hand – strawberries in the other

Body thoroughly used up, totally worn out and

Screaming WOO HOO WHAT A RIDE!!

APRIL

Attitude is the mind's paintbrush.
It can colour any situation.

TUESDAY 1

Struggle is a choice. Choose joy instead

Life is precious so do not let it dribble
between your fingers like sand.

GOALS FOR THIS MONTH

HAPPINESS IS BEING OWNED BY A CAT

APRIL

When one door of happiness closes another opens, but often we look so long at the closed door we do not see that one has been opened for us.

Helen Keller

WEDNESDAY 2

Deal with a bad habit

THURSDAY 3

Face the reality of the world with courage

FRIDAY 4

Be great in little things

AS FOR THE PASSIONS OF THE MIND —

Avoid envy
Avoid anxious fears
Avoid anger and fretting inward
Avoid sadness not communicated
Entertain hopes
Entertain mirth
Entertain delights
Entertain wonder
Entertain admiration

Francis Bacon

APRIL

There is no better time than right now to be happy. Happiness is a journey, not a destination. So, work like you don't need money, love like you've never been hurt, and dance like no one's watching.

SATURDAY 5

Belief in limits creates limited people

SUNDAY 6

Light a candle in memory of someone you loved

MONDAY 7

Live within your budget

Seven Deadly Sins

1. Wealth without work

2. Pleasure without conscience

3. Knowledge without character

4. Commerce without
   morality (ethics)

5. Science without humanity

6. Religion without vision

7. Politics without principals

Mahatma Gandhi

APRIL

Most people fail in life because they major in minor things.

Anthony Hopkins

TUESDAY 8

Give someone a pleasant surprise

WEDNESDAY 9

Do the things you don't like doing first

THURSDAY 10

Your beliefs create your own reality

We could learn a lot from crayons:

some are sharp, some are pretty,

some are dull, some have weird names,

and all are different colours . . .

but they all exist very nicely in the same box.

 **APRIL**

People who say it cannot be done should not interrupt those who are doing it.

FRIDAY 11

Crown each day with some good action

SATURDAY 12

There is always room for improvement

SUNDAY 13

Have a good soak in the bath

MONDAY 14

If you fear something go out and do it

TUESDAY 15

Thoughts become things

It takes a minute to have a crush on someone. An hour to like someone.
A day to love someone.
But . . . A lifetime to forget someone.

HANDPRINTS

Sometimes you get discouraged
Because I am so small
And leave my handprints
On furniture and walls.
But everyday I'm growing
I'll be grown up one day
And all those tiny handprints
Will sadly fade away
So here's a little handprint
So you can recall
Exactly how my fingers
Looked when I was very small.

All the world is a bit strange, except thou and I
Even thou is a bit strange sometimes!

Guard well your spare moments. They
are like uncut diamonds. Discard them
and their value will never be known.
Improve them and they will become the
brightest gems in a useful life.
                    Ralf Waldo Emerson

APRIL

There is no better way to
enjoy the pleasure
of shared company
than over shared food.

WEDNESDAY 16

Eat right

THURSDAY 17

Don't forget your roots

FRIDAY 18

Take time to get a grasp of what is really important

SATURDAY 19

Sing in the shower

SUNDAY 20

Don't complicate your life

MONDAY 21

A caring nature will win the day

REMEMBER YOUR LABEL: MADE BY GOD

 **APRIL**

"I can resist everything
except temptation."
Oscar Wilde
Lady Windermere's Fan

TUESDAY 22

Develop your interests

WEDNESDAY 23

Tenderness and kindness are manifestations of strength

THURSDAY 24

Take 15 minutes to appreciate nature

 *I love You*

A house is not a home
unless you can write
"I LOVE YOU"
on the furniture.

ALL THAT YOU GIVE
IS GIVEN TO
YOURSELF

APRIL

WE LEARN THE TRUTH
THROUGH THE
TEARS WE CRY

FRIDAY 25

Be an encourager

SATURDAY 26

The harder you work the more you can play

SUNDAY 27

YOU MAKE A DIFFERENCE – YOU COUNT

MONDAY 28

Dance with nature

TUESDAY 29

Create, connect, convert

The future belongs to the risk takers, not the security seekers. The more you seek security, the less of it you will have — and the more you pursue opportunity, the more security you will achieve.

APRIL

Some men see things as they are and say "why?". I dream of things that never were and say "why not?".
George Bernard Shaw

WEDNESDAY 30

Give your fears to the wind

Every day:
work for eight hours,
sleep for eight hours
and play for eight hours

In every old person
there is a young person
wondering what happened

I have learnt to live each day
as it comes and not to borrow
trouble by dreading tomorrow.
Dorothy Dix

GOALS FOR MAY

Hitch your wagon to a star.

SACHI

Soon after her little bother was born, little
Sachi began to ask her parents to leave her
alone with the new baby. They worried
that like most four−year−olds, she might feel
jealous and want to hit or shake him, so they
said no. But she showed no signs of jealousy.
She treated the baby with kindness and her
pleas to be left alone with him became more
urgent. They decided to allow it.
Elated, she went into the baby's room and shut
the door, but it opened a crack − enough for her
curious parents to peek in and listen. They saw
little Sachi walk quietly up to her baby brother,
put her face close to his and say quietly
"Baby, tell me what God feels like. I'm
starting to forget."

MAY

Cherish your children for what they are, not for what you'd like them to be.

THURSDAY 1

Give a little of yourself to the community

BE YOURSELF

The world would like to change you;
There are pressures all around
You must decide just who you are,
Then firmly stand your ground.

You have an image of yourself,
An ideal sense of you;
And to this vision you must always
Struggle to be true.

You know what you are good at,
And you know where your talents lie;
But if you're ruled by others,
Your uniqueness could pass by.

Remember, there is much to learn;
But all new things aren't good.
Wisdom lies in what you've learned
And what you have withstood.

Don't gather possessions – gather experiences and adventures, they are so much more exciting.

MAY

Education makes a people
easy to lead, but difficult to drive;
easy to govern, but impossible
to enslave.   *Lord Brougham*

Don't take guilt trips. Take a trip to the Mall,
even to another county, or a foreign country but
NOT to where the guilt is.

FRIDAY 2

Avoid self pity

SATURDAY 3

'One day' is far away

PEOPLE FIRST

Go to the people,
Live with them, Love them
Start with what they know,
Build with what they have,
With the best leaders,
When the work is done,

The task is accomplished,
The people will say:
"WE HAVE DONE
THIS OURSELVES"
Lau Tsu – China 700BC

 **MAY**

If A is a success in life,
then A equals x plus y plus z.
Work is x; y is play;
and z is keeping your mouth shut.
Albert Einstein

SUNDAY 4

Find a simple pleasure today

MONDAY 5

Forgiveness heals a broken heart

TUESDAY 6

Think about what you want, not about what you do not want

WEDNESDAY 7

Buy yourself a herb plant

THURSDAY 8

The most important moment in your life is now

 DO MORE THAN EXIST - LIVE
DO MORE THAN TOUCH - FEEL
DO MORE THAN LOOK - SEE
DO MORE THAN HEAR - LISTEN
DO MORE THAN TALK - SAY SOMETHING

BE A GOOD FRIEND

A friend should be radical;
They should love you when you're
    unlovable,
and bear you when you're
    unbearable.

A friend should be fanatical;
They should cheer you when the
    whole world boos,
Dance when you get good news,
And cry when you cry too.

But most of all,
A friend should be mathematical,
They should multiply the joy,
Divide the sorrow,
Subtract the past,
And add to tomorrow,
Calculate the need deep in your heart,
And always be bigger than the
     sum total of all their parts.

The only real antidote to fear, worry, anger, and doubt is positive action toward the achievement of some worthwhile ideal.

FRIDAY 9

Avoid jumping to hasty conclusions

SATURDAY 10

Within crisis are the seeds of new opportunity

SUNDAY 11

Have breakfast in bed

MONDAY 12

Setting goals make dreams come true

TUESDAY 13

Obstacles strengthen us

WEDNESDAY 14

Send postcards to 3 friends

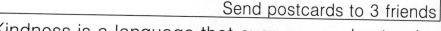

Kindness is a language that everyone understands.

MAY

It often requires more courage to do right, than to fear to do wrong.

Abraham Lincoln

THURSDAY 15

When people are rude, keep your cool

FRIDAY 16

Try your skills at compiling a family tree

SATURDAY 17

Start a book of happy memories

"When I was a boy of fourteen, my father was so ignorant I could hardly stand the old man around. But when I got to be twenty one, I was astonished at how much he had learnt in seven years."

Mark Twain

Winston Churchill once wrote, "Courage is rightly considered the foremost of virtues, for upon it, all others depend."

MAY

Never does the human soul appear so strong and noble as when it forgoes revenge and dares to forgive an injury. *Edwin Hubbell Chapin*

SUNDAY 18

Play fair

MONDAY 19

Your life is a mirror of your consistent thoughts

TUESDAY 20

Assess your strengths accurately

WEDNESDAY 21

Seek and find the beauty all around you

THURSDAY 22

Watch the sun set this evening

A life spent making mistakes is not only more honourable but more useful than a life spent doing nothing. *George Bernard Shaw*

MAY

> Only those who dare to fail greatly can ever achieve greatly.
>
> *Robert F Kennedy*

FRIDAY 23

Hunger finds no fault with cooking

SATURDAY 24

Accepting responsibility is the key to personal freedom

SUNDAY 25

Reach out to others – take the first step

MONDAY 26

Joy uplifts the spirit and creates peace wherever it goes

TUESDAY 27

Your reputation is not raised by lowering others

WEDNESDAY 28

Don't be shy to say you're sorry

Life is not one game, it is a whole season . . . Never give up!

MAY

Don't live down to expectations. Go out there and do something remarkable. *Marcus Valerius Martial*

THURSDAY 29

Happiness is within you, not out there

FRIDAY 30

Find peace in your garden

OUR DEEPEST FEAR

Our deepest fear is not that we are inadequate.
Our deepest fear is that we are powerful beyond measure.
It is our light, not our darkness, that most frightens us.
We ask ourselves, who am I to be –
brilliant, gorgeous, talented, fabulous?
Actually who are you not to be!
You are a child of God.
Your playing small does not serve the world.
There is nothing enlightening about shrinking so that
    people won't feel unsure around you.
We are born to make manifest the Glory of
    God that is within us.
It is not in some of us; it is in everyone.
As we let our own light shine, we unconsciously give other
people permission to do the same.
As we are liberated from our own fears, our presence
    automatically liberates others.
As quoted by Nelson Mandela in his 1994 inaugural speech

MAY

SATURDAY 31

Remember people's names

THE INVITATION

It doesn't interest me what you do for a living. I want to know what you ache for and if you dare to dream of meeting your heart's longing. It doesn't interest me how old you are. I want to know if you will risk looking like a fool for love, for your dream, for the adventure of being alive. It doesn't interest me what planets are squaring your moon. I want to know if you have touched the centre of your own sorrow, if you have been opened by life's betrayals or have become shrivelled and closed from fear of further pain. I want to know if you can sit with pain, mine or your own, without moving to hide it or fade it or fix it. I want to know if you can be with joy, mine or your own, if you can dance with wildness and let the ecstasy fill you to the tips of your fingers and toes without cautioning us to be careful.

It doesn't interest me if the story you are telling is true. I want to know if you can disappoint another to be true to yourself; if you can bear the accusation of betrayal and not betray your own soul; if you can be faithless and therefore trustworthy. I want to know if you can live with failure, yours and mine, and still stand on the edge of the lake and shout to the silver of the moon. It doesn't interest me where you live or how much money you have. I want to know if you can get up, after the night of grief and despair, weary and bruised to the bone, and do what needs to be done to feed the children. I want to know if you can be alone with yourself and if you truly like the company you keep in the empty moments.

Oriah Mountain Dreamer

GOALS FOR NEXT MONTH

 Surround yourself with what you love, whether it is family, pets, keepsakes, music, plants, hobbies, whatever. Your home is your refuge.

Happiness keeps You Sweet,
Trials keep You Strong,
Sorrows keep You Human,
Failures keeps You Humble,
Success keeps You Glowing,
But only **Spirit** keeps You Going!

JUNE

"If you educate
a woman, you have
educated a population"
Kiganda proverb

SUNDAY 1
Don't demand because you're stronger

MONDAY 2
Remember someone's birthday

TUESDAY 3
Write your troubles down and burn them

WEDNESDAY 4
Learn a new skill

THURSDAY 5
Don't cheat, Don't lie, Don't pretend

THE A B C OF RELATIONSHIPS

ACCEPTS YOU AS YOU ARE
BELIEVES IN YOU
CALLS TO SAY HELLO

DOESN'T GIVE UP ON YOU
ENVISIONS THE WHOLE OF YOU
FORGIVES YOUR MISTAKES

JUNE

MUSIC IS
LOVE
IN SEARCH OF
A WORLD

FRIDAY 6

Love deeply

SATURDAY 7

Make a CD of all your favourite music

SUNDAY 8

Remember you always have choices

MONDAY 9

Pain is inevitable, suffering is a choice

TUESDAY 10

Find a new friend

WEDNESDAY 11

Say those words, don't let the moment pass

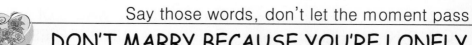

DON'T MARRY BECAUSE YOU'RE LONELY

THE GREATEST LOVE OF ALL

I believe that children are our future
Teach them well, let them lead the way
Show them all the beauty they possess inside
Give them a sense of pride to make it easier
Let the children's laughter remind us how we used to be

Everybody is searching for a hero.
People need someone to look up to
I never found anyone to fulfil my need
A lonely place to be; and so, I learned to depend on me

I decided long ago never to walk in anyone's shadow
If I fail, If I succeed
At least I live, as I believed
No matter what they take from me.
They can't take away my dignity

Because the Greatest love of all, was happening to me
I found the greatest love of all inside of me
The greatest love of all is easy to achieve
Learning to love yourself is the greatest love of all

And if by chance that special place
that you've been dreaming of
leads you to a lonely place
find your strength in love

Written by: Michael Masser and Linda Creed
A wonderful song sung by George Benson

JUNE

When you become educated you don't change, everybody else does. *Kirk Douglas*

THURSDAY 12

Visit the neighbours

FRIDAY 13

Plan a family outing to look forward to

SATURDAY 14

Do what you have to do even at society's scorn

WISDOM HAS TWO PARTS

- HAVING PLENTY TO SAY
- NOT SAYING IT

DON'T GROW OLD, JUST GROW YOU

JUNE

WHAT WE HAVE,
WE HOLD NOT
ONE INCH.

Tommy Devlin

SUNDAY 15

Pick some wild flowers

MONDAY 16

Clear out clutter

TUESDAY 17

A simple rule whenever you are in doubt: Be kind.

WEDNESDAY 18

Map your life's journey with vigour and intelligence

THURSDAY 19

Add passion to what you do

GOALS ARE THE ROADMAPS
TO SUCCESS

 **JUNE**

When we develop the habit of courage and unshakable self-confidence, a whole new world of possibilities opens up to us.

FRIDAY 20
Walk barefoot

SATURDAY 21
Make someone a greeting card

SUNDAY 22
Don't lose faith in God

 ## The reason for life . . .

I don't know how to say it, but somehow it seems to me
That maybe we are stationed where God wants us to be;
That the little place I'm filling is the reason for my birth,
"And you must do the work I do", he sent me down to earth.
If God had wanted otherwise, I reckon he'd have made
Me just a little different, of a worse or better grade; And,
since God knows and understands all things of land and sea,
I fancy that he placed me here, just where he wanted me.
Sometimes, I get to thinking, as my labours I review,
That I should like a higher place with greater things to do;
But I come to the conclusion, when the envying is stilled,
That the post to which God sent me is the post he wanted filled.
So, I plod along and struggle in the hope, when day is through
That I'm really necessary to the things God wants to do,
And there isn't any service I can give, which I should scorn,
For it may just be the reason God allowed that I be born.

JUNE

Most of our future lies ahead.
Denny Crum,
American football coach

MONDAY 23

Don't associate with people you can't trust

TUESDAY 24

Do something positive for yourself

WEDNESDAY 25

Procrastination is the thief of time

THURSDAY 26

Go on that trip, don't postpone it

FRIDAY 27

Visit someone who is lonely

SATURDAY 28

Tell people you love them at every opportunity

Treat your family as you would a special guest.

JUNE

Don't let yesterday's failures bankrupt today's efforts

SUNDAY 29

Be true to yourself

MONDAY 30

Don't put your life on hold

I AM THANKFUL FOR . . .

The mess I have to clean up after a party, it means I have friends
The taxes I have to pay, it means that I have a job.
The clothes that fit me tightly, it means I have enough food to eat
A lawn that needs cutting, windows that need cleaning, guttering
that needs fixing — it means that I have a home.
The parking space I find on the far side of the parking lot —
it means that I can walk.
My huge electricity bill, it means that I am clean and warm.
The piles of laundry and ironing, it means that
I have clothes to wear.
I am thankful for the complaining I hear about our government,
it means that I have freedom of speech.
I appreciate the fact that I can read this message —
it means that I can read.
I am thankful for weariness and aching muscles at the end of
the day — it means that I have been productive,
and the alarm that goes off in the morning —

IT MEANS THAT I AM ALIVE

Goals for July

Change does not cause pain.
It is the resistance to change
that causes pain.

ALL I NEED TO KNOW I LEARNT FROM NOAH'S ARK

1.   Don't miss the boat.
2.   Remember that we are all in the same boat.
3.   Plan ahead. It was not raining when Noah built the ark.
4.   Stay fit, when you are 600 years old someone may ask you to do something big.
5.   Don't listen to critics, just get on with it.
6.   Build your future on high ground.
7.   For safety's sake, travel in pairs.
8.   Speed is not always an advantage.
9.   When you're stressed, float a while.
10.   Remember, the Ark was built by amateurs, the Titanic by professionals.
11.   No matter the storm, when you are with God, there is always a rainbow waiting.

# JULY

Teach us to delight in simple things.

Rudyard Kipling

 Make more inner journeys – Discover who you are, and give yourself time for greater spiritual growth.

TUESDAY 1

Write things down

WEDNESDAY 2

Don't commit when you're not ready

THURSDAY 3

Don't overdose on duty

---

5 GOLDEN RULES TO MAKE YOUR LIFE EASIER:

1. DO IT NOW
2. BE PREPARED WELL IN ADVANCE
3. WORK AT YOUR OWN PACE
4. DON'T AIM FOR PERFECTION
5. SORT OUT YOUR PRIORITIES

JULY

Keep your face to the sunshine –
and you cannot see the shadow.

Helen Keller

FRIDAY 4

Teach by showing, learn by doing

SATURDAY 5

Let those who love you help you

SUNDAY 6

Re-experience happy memories

MONDAY 7

It's important to feel good

TUESDAY 8

If you want the fruit, climb the tree

WEDNESDAY 9

We all work with one infinite power

THE LARGEST ROOM IN THE WORLD
IS THE ROOM FOR IMPROVEMENT

FOR MOTHERS WHO ARE NO LONGER WITH US

In tears we saw you sinking, and watched you pass away.
Our hearts were almost broken, we wanted you to stay.
But when we saw you sleeping, so peaceful, free from pain,
How could we wish you back with us, to suffer that again.

It broke our hearts to lose you, but you did not go alone.
For part of us went with you, the day God took you home.
If roses grow in heaven, please pick a bunch for me.
Place them in my mother's arms and tell her they're from me.

Tell her that I love and miss her, and when she turns to smile,
Place a kiss upon her cheek and hold her for a while.
Remembering her is easy, I do it every day,
But there is an ache within my heart that will never go away.

Don't think of her as gone away, her journey has just begun.
Life holds so many facets. this earth is only one.
Just think of her as resting, from the sorrows and the tears.
In a place of warmth and comfort,
where there are no days or years.

Think how she must be wishing, that we could know today,
That nothing but our sadness could really pass away.
Think of her as living, in the hearts of those she touched.
For nothing loved is ever lost, and she is loved so very much!

JULY

Whatever the mind
can conceive,
it can achieve.
W.Clement stone

THURSDAY 10

Things are not always as they appear to be

FRIDAY 11

Life is meant to be abundant in all areas

SATURDAY 12

Criticism is just another person's opinion

First I was dying to finish high school and start college.
Then I was dying to finish college and start working.
Then I was dying to marry and have children.
Then I was dying for my children to grow old enough
    for school so I could go back to work.
Then I was dying to retire.
Now I am dying, and I have suddenly
    realised that I forgot to **live.**   *Author unknown*

JULY

Happiness is self-discovery
Happiness is being yourself
Happiness is creating
Happiness is enjoying
   what you have
Happiness is friendship
Happiness is optional
Happiness is your choice
Practice to be happy

SUNDAY 13
Use your talents

MONDAY 14
Always believe in miracles

TUESDAY 15
Give someone a surprise

WEDNESDAY 16
Love your life

THURSDAY 17
Talk less and listen more

JULY

Nothing is by chance
everything is a lesson
to learn.

FRIDAY 18

Stress degrades your body

SATURDAY 19

Slow down

SUNDAY 20

Your attitude controls your life

MONDAY 21

Make a commitment

TUESDAY 22

It's never too soon to be kind, but it can be too late

WEDNESDAY 23

Learn to become still

GET IT TOGETHER AND THEN REMEMBER
WHERE YOU PUT IT

JULY

Nothing will ever be attempted if all possible objections must first be overcome. *samuel Johnson*

THURSDAY 24

Differences enrich families

FRIDAY 25

Are your thoughts worthy of you?

SATURDAY 26

Everyone deserves to be understood

SUNDAY 27

Mind your own business

. . . When people have light in themselves, it will shine out from them. Then we get to know each other as we walk together in the darkness, without needing to pass our hands over each other's faces, or to intrude into each other's hearts

JULY

Most notable winners have encountered heartbreaking obstacles.

MONDAY 28

Tidy your cupboard

TUESDAY 29

Communication oils the wheels of relationships

WEDNESDAY 30

Have a healthy respect for yourself

THURSDAY 31

Pay your bills with a grateful heart

~Beauty of a Woman~
The beauty of a woman is not in the clothes she wears,
The figure she carries, or the way she combs her hair.
The beauty of a woman must be seen from her eyes,
Because that is the doorway to her heart,
The place where love resides.
The beauty of a woman Is not in a facial mole,
But true beauty in a woman is reflected in her soul.
It is the caring that she lovingly gives,
The passion that she shows.
The beauty of a woman
With passing years -- only grows.

MUD PUDDLES AND DANDELIONS

When I look at a patch of dandelions, I see a bunch of weeds that are going to take over my yard. My kids see flowers for Mum and blowing white fluff you can wish on.

When I look at an old drunk and he smiles at me, I see a smelly dirty person who wants money and I look away. My kids see someone smiling at them and they smile back.

When I hear music I love, I know I can't carry a tune and don't have much rhythm, so I self-consciously listen. My kids feel the beat and move to it. They sing out the words and if they don't know them, they make up their own.

When I feel the wind on my face, I brace myself against it. I feel it messing up my hair and pulling me back when I walk. My kids close their eyes, spread their arms and fly with it, until they fall to the ground laughing.

When I pray, I say thee and thou and grant me this, give me that. My kids say, "Hi God! Thanks for my toys and my friends. Please keep the bad dreams away tonight! Sorry, I don't want to go to Heaven yet. I would miss my Mummy and Daddy."

When I see a mud puddle, I step around it. I see muddy shoes and dirty carpets. My kids sit in it. They see dams to build, rivers to cross and worms to play with.

I wonder if we are given children to teach or to learn from? No wonder God loves the little children!!

Enjoy the little things in life, for one day you may look back and realise they were the big things.

Just a reminder about the important things in life . . . I wish you mud puddles and dandelions.

Some people come into our lives
and quickly go.
Others stay a while –
leave footprints in our hearts
and we are never, ever the same.

Goals for AUGUST

Set a goal so big,
that if you achieved it,
it would blow your mind.

THE WINDS OF GRACE BLOW ALL THE TIME
ALL WE NEED TO DO IS SET OUR SAILS
RAMAKRISHNA

AUGUST

By the time you make
the ends meet,
they move the ends!

FRIDAY 1

Don't let the world spin you out of control

SATURDAY 2

It is easier to ask for forgiveness than permission

SUNDAY 3

Appreciate the accomplishments of others

The past always looks better when you look back on it than it did at the time. The present never looks as good as it did in the future. But, it is depressing to think back to good times too often, as you think you'd never have anything as good again.

TEN ROSES FOR YOU

🌹One rose for friendship

🌹A second one for love

🌹One for financial wealth

🌹One for happiness

🌹One for success

🌹One for knowledge

🌹One for beauty

🌹One for the family

🌹One for honesty

🌹And the last one for a long
and healthy life

God sent each person into the world with a
special message to deliver, a special song to sing
and a special act of love to bestow . . . no one
else can speak my message or sing my song or
offer my love . . . these are entrusted to me.

Author unknown

AUGUST

COURAGE doesn't always roar, sometimes courage is the little voice at the end of the day that says: "I'll try again tomorrow"

MONDAY 4

Develop a forgiving attitude

TUESDAY 5

Delays can be a chance to think and regroup

WEDNESDAY 6

Create a vision board of what you want to attract

THURSDAY 7

Think before you act

FRIDAY 8

Be the change you want to see in the world

"We are not human beings having a spiritual experience we are spiritual beings having a human experience"

Teilhard de Chardin

AUGUST

Don't worry what people think. They don't do it very often!

SATURDAY 9

You can move mountains, but you need a good shovel

SUNDAY 10

Meditate with good music

MONDAY 11

Feed your pot plants

TUESDAY 12

We make the rules on size and time

WEDNESDAY 13

Walk tall

THURSDAY 14

Head off minor misunderstandings before they develop

Problems become smaller when you embrace them as part of life.

AUGUST

God made wrinkles to show where SMILES have been.

FRIDAY 15

Check your priorities

SATURDAY 16

Stop and smell the roses

SUNDAY 17

Walk your talk

MONDAY 18

Practice contentment

TUESDAY 19

When you fall in love, it shows

WEDNESDAY 20

Deal with unfinished business

Only in the dictionary does Success come before Work

Two Days Without Worry

There are two days in every week about which we should not worry, two days which should be kept free from fear and apprehension. One of these days is Yesterday with all its mistakes and cares, its faults and blunders, its aches and pains.
Yesterday has passed forever beyond our control.
All the money in the world cannot bring back Yesterday.
We cannot undo a single act we performed; We cannot erase a single word we said. Yesterday is gone forever.

The other day we should not worry about is Tomorrow

with all its possible adversities, its burdens, its large promise and its poor performance;
Tomorrow is also beyond our immediate control.
Tomorrow's sun will rise, either in splendour or behind a mask of clouds, but it will rise. Until it does, we have no stake in Tomorrow, for it is yet to be born.

This leaves only one day, Today.

Any person can fight the battle of just one day.
It is when you and I add the burdens of those two awful eternities, Yesterday and Tomorrow that we break down.
It is not the experience of Today that drives a person mad, it is the remorse or bitterness of something which happened Yesterday and the dread of what Tomorrow may bring.

Let us, therefore, Live but one day at a time.

AUGUST

If you want to find the most comfortable spot in the house, you'd have to move the cat.

THURSDAY 21

Get enough sleep

FRIDAY 22

Life is for living

SATURDAY 23

Start a new hobby

Tomorrow is another day

 HAPPY HOME RECIPE

4 cups of Love
2 cups of Loyalty
3 cups of Forgiveness
1 cup of Friendship
5 spoons of Hope
2 teaspoons of Tenderness
4 quarts of Faith
1 barrel of Laughter

Mix Love and Loyalty with Faith. Blend with Tenderness, Kindness and Understanding. Add Friendship and Hope. Sprinkle abundantly with Laughter. Bake it with Sunshine. Serve daily with a generous heart.

AUGUST

"I can live for 2 months on one good compliment"
Mark Twain

SUNDAY 24

Cherish your freedom

MONDAY 25

Let go of negativity

TUESDAY 26

You're guided by your mind

WEDNESDAY 27

Give up on guilt

THURSDAY 28

Allocate time with your family

People are always blaming circumstances for what they are.
I do not believe in circumstances. The people who get on in
this world are the people who get up and look for the
circumstances they want, and if they cannot find them,
make them.   *George Bernard Shaw*

AUGUST

OUR REMEDIES OFT IN OURSELVES DO LIE.

William Shakespeare

FRIDAY 29

Be kinder than necessary

SATURDAY 30

Live Simply

HOPE

Hope looks for the good in people instead of harping on the worst.

Hope opens doors where despair closes them.

Hope discovers what can be done instead of grumbling about what cannot.

Hope draws its power from a deep trust in God and the basic goodness in humankind.

Hope lights a candle instead of "cursing the darkness".

Hope regards problems, small and large, as opportunities.

Hope cherishes no illusions, nor does it yield to cynicism.

Hope sets big goals and is not frustrated by repeated difficulties or setbacks.

Hope pushes ahead when it would be easy to quit.

Hope puts up with modest gains, realising that the longest journey starts with the first step.

Hope accepts misunderstandings as the price for serving the greater good of others.

Hope is a good loser because it has the divine assurance of final victory.

AUGUST

Who can then so softly
bind the wounds of another
as he who has felt the same
wound himself.   *Jefferson*

SUNDAY 31

Focus on being grateful for what you already have

GOALS FOR SEPTEMBER

Live as if it is your last day,
Plan as if you're going to
live forever.

Map out your life's journey with vigour + intelligence

IF I HAD MY LIFE OVER

(In memory of Erma Bombeck, a mother who lost her fight with cancer.)

I would have talked less and listened more.

I would have invited friends over to dinner, even if the carpet was stained and the sofa faded.

I would have eaten the popcorn in the good living room and worried much less about the dirt when someone wanted to light a fire in the fireplace.

I would have taken the time to listen to my grandfather ramble on about his youth.

I would never have insisted the car windows be rolled up on a summer's day because my hair had just been done.

I would have burned the pink candle sculpted like a rose before it melted in storage.

I would have sat on the lawn with my children and not worried about grass stains.

I would have cried and laughed less while watching television and more while watching life.

I would have shared more of the responsibility carried by my husband.

I would have gone to bed when I was sick instead of pretending that the world would go into a holding pattern if I weren't there for the day.

I would never have bought anything just because it was practical, wouldn't show soil or was guaranteed to last a lifetime.

Instead of wishing away nine months of pregnancy, I'd have cherished every moment and realised that it was the only chance I had in assisting God with a miracle.

When my kids wanted to kiss me impetuously, I would never have said, "Later, now go wash up for dinner."

There would have been more "I love you's" and more "I'm sorry's" but given another shot at life, I would seize every minute ⋯ Look at it, hold it and never give it back.

SEPTEMBER

SOMETIMES SILENCE
IS THE BEST ANSWER

MONDAY 1

Create a scrap book of all your ideals

TUESDAY 2

Be the peace maker if you have a conflict with someone

WEDNESDAY 3

Make new friends

THURSDAY 4

Make a wish

FRIDAY 5

Invite someone over for dinner

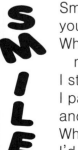

Smiling is infectious;
you catch it like the flu,
When someone smiled at
    me today,
I started smiling too.
I passed around the corner,
and someone saw my grin,
When he smiled I realised
I'd passed it on to him.

I thought about that smile,
then I realised its worth
A single smile, just like mine,
could travel round the earth.
So if you feel a smile begin,
Don't leave it undetected
Let's start the epidemic quick,
and get the world infected!

SEPTEMBER

If there are no dogs in Heaven, then when I die I want to go where they went. *Will Rogers*

SATURDAY 6

Take a posy of flowers to a friend

SUNDAY 7

Investigate holistic and natural healing

MONDAY 8

Be forgiving

TUESDAY 9

Work takes as long as the time you have to do it in

WEDNESDAY 10

You can heal your life

THURSDAY 11

Remember the day the world cried

EVERYONE NEEDS RULES AND LIMITS

SEPTEMBER

FOUR-NNULA FOR SUCCESS
1. Show up on time.
2. Do what you say you will do.
3. Finish what you start.
4. Show appreciation.

FRIDAY 12

Create your home into the place you really prefer to be

SATURDAY 13

Do unto others as you would like them to do unto you

SUNDAY 14

Days are made of moments

Do not stand by my grave and weep,
I am not dead, I do not sleep,
I am a thousand winds that blow
I am the diamond glint on snow
I am the sunlight on ripened grain
I am the gentle autumn rain
When you awaken in the morning hush
I am the swift uplifting rush
Of quiet birds in circled light
I am the soft stars that shine at night
Do not stand at my grave and cry
I am not there, I did not die. *ANON*

LIFE IS LIKE MAIL, SOMETIMES YOU JUST DON'T GET IT.

DUST IF YOU MUST . . .

I can't tell you how many countless hours that I have spent CLEANING!

I used to spend at least 8 hours every weekend making sure things were just perfect -

"in case someone came over".

Then I realised one day that no one came over; they were all out living life and having fun

Now, when people visit, I find no need to explain the "condition" of my home.

They are more interested in hearing about the things I've been doing

while I was away living life and having fun.

 If you haven't figured this out yet, please heed this advice.

Life is short. Enjoy it! Dust if you must,

but wouldn't it be better, to paint a picture or write a letter,

 bake a cake or plant a seed, ponder the difference between want and need?

Dust if you must, but there's not much time, with rivers to swim and mountains to climb,

music to hear and books to read, friends to cherish and life to lead.

Dust if you must, but the world's out there with the sun in your eyes, the wind in your ha

a flutter of snow, a shower of rain. This day will not come around again.

Dust if you must, but bear in mind, old age will come and it's not kind.

And when you go - and go you must - you, yourself, will make more dust!

SEPTEMBER

Accept people for what they are.

MONDAY 15
Happiness is an inside job

TUESDAY 16
When you feel down, count your blessings

WEDNESDAY 17
Go swimming

THURSDAY 18
Your thoughts determine how you feel

FRIDAY 19
If you want prosperity, intend it

If the only prayer you say in your whole life is 'thank you', that would suffice.

Meister Eckhart

SEPTEMBER

REMIND YOURSELF:
"I'VE COME A
LONG WAY"

SATURDAY 20

Everybody is entitled to their own opinion

SUNDAY 21

Intuition means inner teacher

MONDAY 22

The cause and the effect is locked up in the same space

TUESDAY 23

Spend a few hours on your own

WEDNESDAY 24

Love generously

THURSDAY 25

If you don't like it − change it

WORK IS NOT PUNISHMENT, IT'S A BLESSING

SEPTEMBER

A good exercise for the heart is to bend down and help another.

FRIDAY 26

Write your own mission statement

SATURDAY 27

Your beliefs create your own reality

SUNDAY 28

Speak kindly

MONDAY 29

Someone is proud of you

TUESDAY 30

Take the time to get a medical check-up

Our doubts are traitors and make us lose the good we oft might win, by fearing to attempt.

William Shakespeare

GOALS FOR OCTOBER

Send my mother an angel

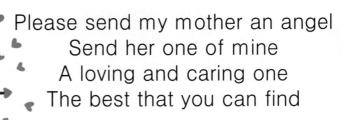

Please send my mother an angel
Send her one of mine
A loving and caring one
The best that you can find

Please send my mother an angel
And trust her with its care
Someone or something for her to love
And to always be there

OCTOBER

If we want to build a better world, we need to start with individuals.

WEDNESDAY 1

Always try to see the big picture

THURSDAY 2

Have tea with a friend

FRIDAY 3

Visit your local library

HAPPINESS CAKE

1 cup good thoughts
1 cup of kind deeds
1 cup of consideration
   for others

2 cups of sacrifice
2 cups of well beaten
   faults
3 cups of forgiveness

Mix thoroughly. Add tears of joy, sorrow and sympathy. Flavour with love and kindly service. Fold in 4 cups of prayer and faith. Blend well. Fold into daily life. Bake well with the warmth of human kindness and serve with a smile at any time. It will satisfy the hunger of many starved souls.

OCTOBER

Men are from earth.
Women are from earth.
Deal with it.

SATURDAY 4

Make plans for the weekend

SUNDAY 5

Be effective

MONDAY 6

Intuition is a spiritual faculty

TUESDAY 7

Two people working together creates an invisible third

WEDNESDAY 8

Spirit works on a fulltime basis

THURSDAY 9

Put first things first

Good judgement comes from experience and experience comes
from bad judgement. *Barry LePatner*

OCTOBER

Faith is like a muscle...
Exercise it to make
it strong!

FRIDAY 10

Bake a cake for an elderly person

SATURDAY 11

There are losses which are gains, and gains which are losses

SUNDAY 12

Find a simple pleasure today

"When you develop yourself to the point where your belief in yourself is so strong that you know that you can accomplish anything you put your mind to, your future will be unlimited." *Brian Tracy*

OCTOBER

CLEAR OUT THE CLUTTER!

MONDAY 13

Take time to phone an old friend

TUESDAY 14

Failure to forgive can become an unnecessary burden

WEDNESDAY 15

Your ability to create positive thoughts is unlimited

THURSDAY 16

Reflect on past pleasures

FRIDAY 17

Nothing is impossible

By clearing your living and working space, you are allowing new energy to come into your life. We keep more material possessions than we need because our direction of life is often scattered and unfocused. Once the clutter is out of your life, you will find it easier to make decisions and enjoy the good things in life.

OCTOBER

Approach love and cooking with reckless abandon.

SATURDAY 18

Create something this week

SUNDAY 19

Happy people carry their sunshine with them

MONDAY 20

Temporary loss often results in permanent gain

TUESDAY 21

Focus on being grateful for what you have

WEDNESDAY 22

Dare to dream

THURSDAY 23

A little job well done is the first step toward a bigger one

NO ONE CAN KEEP ME DOWN BUT MYSELF

HOW VERY SPECIAL YOU ARE!

Your presence is a gift to the world,
You're unique and one of a kind.
Your life can be what you want it to be,
take one day at a time.

Count your blessings, not your troubles.
And you'll make it through what comes along.
Within you are so many answers,
Understand, have courage, be strong.

Don't put limits on yourself,
your dreams are waiting to be realised.
Don't leave your important decisions to chance.
Reach for your goal, your peak and your prize.

Nothing wastes more time than worrying.
The longer a problem is carried the heavier it gets.
Don't take things too seriously -
Live a life of serenity, not a life of regrets.

Remember that a little love goes a long way.
Remember that a lot goes forever.
Remember that friendship is a wise investment.
Life's treasures are people . . . . Together.

Have health and hope and happiness.
Take the time to wish on a star.
And don't forget for even a day - - -
HOW SPECIAL YOU ARE!

OCTOBER

The sole purpose of a child's middle name is so he can tell when he's really in trouble.

FRIDAY 24

Deal with yourself

SATURDAY 25

Self acceptance is the doorway to greatness

SUNDAY 26

A kind act is a seed that can grow into a tree

Bride and Groom Pie

One cup of confidence
One cup of love
In a pan of happiness
Mix the above
Add a pinch of tenderness
A tablespoon of trust
Stir well in the sunshine
Roll out the loving crust
Flour with contentment
Keep free from strife
Bake well for life

OCTOBER

"I think it would be a good idea"

Mahatma Ghandi, when asked what he thought of Western Civilisation.

MONDAY 27

Honest competition is stimulating and healthy

TUESDAY 28

Give someone an unexpected hug

WEDNESDAY 29

You're worthy of being loved

THURSDAY 30

Evaluate a situation

FRIDAY 31

Do something you love doing today

Learning is finding out what you already know.
Doing is demonstrating that you know it.
Teaching is reminding others that they
know it too.
We are all learners, doers and teachers.

GOALS FOR NEXT NOVEMBER
Action plans achieve goals

THE THOUGHTS YOU THINK, BECOME THE THINGS OF YOUR LIFE.

NOVEMBER

WHERE THERE IS NO VISION, THE PEOPLE WILL PERISH.

Proverbs 29:18

No man has ever been shot while doing the dishes!

SATURDAY 1	
	Creation is the spice of life
SUNDAY 2	
	Your beliefs determine your thoughts
MONDAY 3	
	Have a visible street number on your gate
TUESDAY 4	
	Crown each day with some good action
WEDNESDAY 5	
	Create something this week

You must be the change you want to see in the world.   *Gandhi*

NOVEMBER

Enthusiasm is the yeast that makes your hopes rise to the stars. Enthusiasm is the sparkle in your eyes, the swing in your gait, the grip of your hand, the irresistible surge of will and energy to execute your ideas. *HENRY FORD*

THURSDAY 6

Only that which is honestly got is gain

A CREED FOR THOSE WHO HAVE SUFFERED

I asked God for strength, that I might achieve.
I was made weak, that I might learn humbly to obey. . .

I asked for health, that I might do great things.
I was given infirmity, that I might do better things. . .

I asked for riches, that I might be happy.
I was given poverty, that I might be wise. . .

I asked for power, that I might enjoy all things.
I was given weakness, that I might feel the need for God. . . .

I asked for all things, that I might enjoy life.
I was given life, that I might enjoy all things. . .

I got nothing I asked for — but every thing I hoped for.
Almost despite myself, my unspoken prayers were answered.
I am, among men, most richly blessed.   *Roy Campanella*

A FRIEND THAT'S ALWAYS THERE

If I could catch a rainbow
I would do it just for you
And share with you its beauty
On the days you're feeling blue

If I could build a mountain
You could call your very own
A place to find serenity
A place to be alone

If I could take your troubles
I would toss them in the sea
But all these things
I'm finding are impossible for me

I cannot build a mountain
Or catch a rainbow fair
But let me be what I know best
A friend that's always there

NOVEMBER

Change occurs when
the pain of hanging
on is greater than
the fear of letting go.

FRIDAY 7	
	Take time to love
SATURDAY 8	
	Indulge in your artistic nature
SUNDAY 9	
	Replace the earth's resources
MONDAY 10	
	Your perception is your reality
TUESDAY 11	
	Learn from the mistakes of others
WEDNESDAY 12	
	Don't believe all you hear

Never jest about another's faults, failures,
misfortunes or handicaps.

NOVEMBER

You are the master of your fate
and the captain of your soul

THURSDAY 13

Thoughts are seeds and seeds are deeds

FRIDAY 14

Good temper oils the wheels of life

SATURDAY 15

We all have all the time there is

IN 1799 VON GOETHE SUGGESTED THAT WE SHOULD PRAY FOR THE FOLLOWING:

Health enough to make work a pleasure.
Wealth enough to support our needs.
Strength enough to battle with difficulties and overcome them.
Grace enough to confess our sins and forsake them.
Patience enough to toil until some good is accomplished.
Charity enough to see some good in our neighbours.
Love enough to move us to be useful and helpful to others.
Faith enough to make real the things of God.
Hope enough to remove all anxious fears concerning the future.

AN ANGEL'S KISS

We go through life so often,
not stopping to enjoy the day.
And we take each one for granted,
As we travel on our way.
For in your pain and sorrow,
An Angel's kiss will help you through.
This kiss is very private,
For it is meant for only you.
We never stop to measure,
Anything we just might miss.
But if the wind should blow by softly,
You'll feel an Angel's kiss.
A kiss that is sent from heaven,
A kiss from up above.
A kiss that is very special,
From someone that you love.
So when your hearts are heavy,
And filled with tears and pain,
And no one can console you,
Remember once again . . .
About the ones you grieve for,
Because you sadly miss.
And the gentle breeze you took for granted,
Was just an Angel's kiss.

NOVEMBER

Beautiful young people are works of nature. Beautiful old people are works of art.

SUNDAY 16

To handle others use your heart

MONDAY 17

Great minds discuss ideas

TUESDAY 18

A good book is a good companion

WEDNESDAY 19

Surround yourself with people that you like and that like you

THURSDAY 20

Make plans for Christmas

There are two things over which you have total control. One is your thoughts, the other is your mouth.

NOVEMBER

Most of us go to our grave with our music still inside of us.

FRIDAY 21	
	You're too special to get angry
SATURDAY 22	
	Keep your house in order
SUNDAY 23	
	Cheer up the entrance to your home
MONDAY 24	
	Invite friends to dinner
TUESDAY 25	
	Don't judge people by their relatives
WEDNESDAY 26	
	Talk slowly but think quickly

SPEND TIME WITH PEOPLE THAT ARE FOR YOU.

NOVEMBER

He who hesitates
is probably right.

THURSDAY 27

Remain warm and approachable

FRIDAY 28

Phone an old friend

SATURDAY 29

Dependability is the first foundation stone of good character

SUNDAY 30

Believe in love at first sight

A FRIEND

Strengthens the heart, repairs the hurt,
encourages the discovery, enlightens
the mind, dissolves the pain, banishes
the loneliness, understands the anxieties,
increases the joy, deepens the spirit and
frees the soul.

CHRISTMAS SHOPPING LIST
(DON'T FORGET TO REMEMBER
SOMEONE OLD OR LONELY)

Sometimes
those who have
given us the most
are the ones
we fail to thank . . .

THANK YOU.

DECEMBER

Happiness is like perfume, if you sprinkle it around, you can't help spilling a few drops on yourself.

MY MOTHER

MONDAY 1

Say out loud 'I LOVE MYSELF'

TUESDAY 2

Miracles do happen

WEDNESDAY 3

Be patient with children

THURSDAY 4

Let your greatness blossom

FRIDAY 5

Visit someone elderly or lonely

 Every child is a gift to us by God. A child is a gift so valuable that we should cherish each and every one and help them develop, so that they can grow into active, well-adjusted and happy adults.

Nelson Mandela

DECEMBER

"Change your life from making a living to *making a difference.*"

SATURDAY 6

Today can be ANYTHING you can imagine

SUNDAY 7

Having a sharp tongue can cut your own throat

MONDAY 8

Plan your work and work your plan

TUESDAY 9

Life is a measure to be filled not a goblet to be drained

WEDNESDAY 10

If you want your dreams to come true, don't oversleep

THURSDAY 11

Think of hopes that lie before you

Don't let yesterday's failures bankrupt today's efforts

DECEMBER

When small stones move landslides can happen.

FRIDAY 12

Believe and succeed

SATURDAY 13

Take a chance

SUNDAY 14

May angels bless you day and night

THE 12 RICHES OF LIFE

1. A positive mental attitude
2. Sound physical health.
3. Harmony in human relationships.
4. Freedom from fear.
5. Hope of achievement.
6. Capacity for faith.
7. Willingness to share ones blessings.
8. A labour of love.
9. An open mind on all subjects.
10. Self Discipline.
11. The capacity to understand people.
12. Economic security.

Napoleon Hill

THERE ARE FIVE KINDS OF PEOPLE

THOSE WHO MAKE THINGS HAPPEN
THOSE WHO WATCH THINGS HAPPEN
THOSE WHO SAY NOTHING HAS EVER HAPPENED
THOSE WHO WONDER WHAT HAPPENED
OSE WHO TALK ABOUT EVERYTHING THAT HAPPENED

The *life*
given us by nature
is short
but the memory
of a well-spent life
is *eternal*   *Cicero*

"Our greatest glory is not in
never failing but in rising up
every time we fail."
Ralph Waldo Emerson

DECEMBER

When we create peace and harmony and balance in our minds, we will find it in our lives. *Louise L. Hay*

MONDAY 15

Time to decorate the Christmas tree

TUESDAY 16

Allow extra time to get to places

WEDNESDAY 17

Build – work – dream – create

THURSDAY 18

Look at a situation broadly

FRIDAY 19

Remember to keep calm and cheerful

CELEBRATE THE HAPPINESS THAT FRIENDS ARE ALWAYS GIVING, MAKE EVERY DAY A HOLIDAY, AND CELEBRATE JUST LIVING!

Amanda Bradley

 # MOTHER CHRISTMAS

Where art thou Mother Christmas, I really wish I knew,
Why Father should get all the praise, and no one
mentions you. I bet you buy the presents, and wrap
them large and small, while all the time the dirty swine
pretends he's done it all. So hail to Mother Christmas,
e uncomplaining slave, And down with Father Christmas,
the good—for—nothing knave.

Roald Dahl

Every Grand—dad
was once a great dad.

TAKE PRIDE IN HOW FAR YOU'VE COME,
HAVE FAITH IN HOW FAR YOU CAN GO.

For last year's words
    belong to last year's language.
        And next year's words await another voice.
            And to make an end is to make a beginning.
            T.S. Elliot. "Little Gidding"

DECEMBER

Call the world, if you please
'The vale of Soul—Making'
Then you will find out the
use of the world.   *John Keats*

SATURDAY 20

A pint of sweat saves a gallon of blood

SUNDAY 21

Things don't matter, people do

MONDAY 22

Life is short, celebrate all you can

TUESDAY 23

For all of us there are turning points in our lives

WEDNESDAY 24

Don't compete—CREATE

THURSDAY 25

Happy Christmas

Tell those dear to you how much you love them.

 **DECEMBER**

KNOWLEDGE IN YOUTH
IS WISDOM IN AGE.

FRIDAY 26

Forge your own path

SATURDAY 27

Aspirations BECOME possibilities

SUNDAY 28

Make and keep promises

Poverty is a state of mind often
introduced by a neighbour's new car.

Friends are quiet angels
who lift us to our feet
when our wings have
forgotten how to fly.

Imagination is a magic
carpet, it can take you
anywhere.

DECEMBER

A life spent making mistakes is not only more honourable but more useful than a life spent doing nothing.
George Bernard Shaw

MONDAY 29
Thinking can change your life

TUESDAY 30
Be all that you can be

WEDNESDAY 31
Spend quality time with your partner

"If you can find a WHY, You can also find a HOW"

"We who lived in the concentration camps can remember the men who walked among the huts comforting others, giving away their last piece of bread. They may have been few in number, but they offer sufficient proof that everything can be taken away from a man but one thing: The last of his freedoms – to choose one's attitude in any given set of circumstances. To choose one's own way."

"Man's Search For Meaning" by Victor Frankl

PLANS AND GOALS FOR 2009

Let your mind be quiet, realising the beauty of the world, and the immense, the boundless treasures that it holds in store.

MAY THE MEMORIES WE GIVE
RECORD THE LIFE THAT WE LIVE.

ORDER FOR THE IRISH GET UP AND GO DIARY 2009

(PRINT IN BLOCK LETTERS)

PLEASE SUPPLY ME WITH _____ 2009 DIARIES
@ €10 EACH, postage and packing included.

NAME_____

ADDRESS_____

_____

_____

Cheque/Postal Order included to the value of _____

Signature

_____

Forward your order to: Glenda Devlin,
8 Burma Road, Strandhill, Co. Sligo
IRELAND

The final forming of a person's character
lies in their own hands.
Anne Frank

GOOD BYE'S

After a while you learn the subtle difference between
holding a hand and chaining a soul; and you learn that
love doesn't mean security. And you begin to learn that
kisses aren't promises and you begin to accept your
defeats with the grace of an adult and not the grief of
a child. And you learn to build all your roads on today
because tomorrow's ground is too uncertain for plans
and futures have a way of falling down in mid flight.
After a while you learn that even sunshine burns if
you ask too much. So plant your own garden and
decorate your own soil instead of waiting for someone
to bring you flowers. And you learn that you really can
endure, that you really are strong and you really have
worth. And you learn and you learn. With every
good-bye … YOU LEARN!   *Adam Ricker*

Address List

Name	Address	Telephone	Birthday
A			
B			
C			
D			
E			
F			

Address List

Name	Address	Telephone	Birthday
G			
H			
I			
J			
K			
L			

Address List

Name	Address	Telephone	Birthday
M			
N			
O			
P			
Q			
R			

Address List

Name	Address	Telephone	Birthday
S			
T			
U			
V			
W			
XYZ			

NOTES

NOTES

NOTES